Published by Influx Press
The Greenhouse
49 Green Lanes, London, N16 9BU
www.influxpress.com / @InfluxPress
All rights reserved.
Text © Paul Scraton, 2021
Photography © Eymelt Sehmer, 2021

This edition 2021.
Printed and bound in the UK by TJ Books.
Paperback ISBN: 9781910312858
Ebook ISBN: 9781910312865

Editor: Gary Budden
Copyeditor: Dan Coxon
Cover design: Vince Haig
Interior design: Vince Haig

# in
# the
# pines

**Paul Scraton**

**Eymelt Sehmer**

Influx Press
London

**ONE**

# ALONE IN THE WOODS

At the age of ten I ran away from home. I don't remember why. Something had happened to trigger it, perhaps with one of my siblings, perhaps with my parents. I remember feeling certain in that moment the only option I had was to leave.

I didn't leave right away. I knew, from the books I had read and my *Explorer's Journal*, which I took everywhere with me, that it was important to be prepared. It was important, the journal said, to make a plan for even the shortest adventure. You had to plan, even if you didn't know where you were going. *Especially* if you didn't know where you were going.

In my room I laid out all the things I would need on top of the bed. The *Explorer's Journal* had a useful packing checklist, and there was space within it to add your own items, so you could plan according to the specifics of your trip.

Binoculars.
Compass.
Penknife.
Whistle.
Magnifying glass.
Notebook.
Pencil.
Spare set of clothes.
Sleeping bag.
Scotch tape.
A length of rope.
Plastic sheet.

With the last couple of items, it would be possible to build a tent. Two sticks, some rocks, and the plastic sheet could be transformed into a shelter for the night. Any adventurer worth anything knew that. The plastic sheet was the only item I did not have to hand, so I sneaked downstairs and into the garage, searching out, from among the boxes piled high on metal shelves, the groundsheet from the huge frame tent my parents had bought for a summer trip. We used it on that holiday and never again.

With the groundsheet added to the pile of things on my bed, I was ready to start packing. My school rucksack was easily big enough, and even with everything stuffed inside, it wasn't all that heavy. I stood in the middle of my room, the rucksack on my back, looking in the mirror, proud that I was both travelling light and travelling prepared. From the piggybank on the windowsill I emptied out all I owned into a small sandwich bag, and stuffed it down into the depths of my rucksack. From the bathroom I took a full toilet roll, threading it through with one of the straps from my bag. And from the kitchen I took the final banana in the fruit bowl. I was ready.

♦  ♦  ♦

The narrow path that ran beyond our fence at the bottom of the garden offered two options, two routes away from the place I was leaving forever. The first was down towards the main road and on, into the town centre. The second would lead me past the gardens of our estate to a scruffy patch of wasteland between the last of the houses and the start of the forest. It was where the bottle banks stood in a fat line, the ground in front of them churned by cars turning in this dead end. But unless you had something with which to feed the open mouths of the bottle banks there was no need to go down there, and I knew that for my mission to be a success I had to get away from the place where people might recognise me. Spotted early, it could all be over before it had even begun. Through the gate at the bottom of the garden I turned right, aiming for the wasteland, the bottle banks and the trees. The forest it was.

I moved quickly, only slowing my pace once I had crossed the open ground and entered the embrace of the woods. The footpath ran off ahead of me in a straight line, rising and falling with the shape of the land between a mixed forest of trees. Birch and oak, beech and pine. I knew this patch of woodland well; it was one I had visited many times, whether on walks with my parents or on an afternoon outing from the primary school. But I had never been in here on my own, and it only took a few steps along the path before I was afraid.

I wouldn't have been able to explain it if someone had asked me at the time, but looking back, it was the accumulated drip-feed of knowledge about the forest and what it contained; the things that could happen beneath the canopy when you were hidden away from the rest of the world. There were songs and rhymes, books and films, whispered stories heard in the playground and half-remembered fairy tales. Alone in the forest, nerves rising from the bottom of my stomach, I was hyper aware of my surroundings. It was the first time I had experienced this, noticing and taking in all that was happening around me. The ants crossing the path in hurrying lines. The sound of my feet, crunching shells of fallen beech nuts. The trees, moving high above my head to make a sound of the sea, of waves crashing against the shore. It was the sound of a previous holiday, remembered in the woods, far from the sea.

♦   ♦   ♦

After a few hundred metres I stepped off the path and sat down on the thick, exposed roots of an old tree. I could hear the birds, the gentle song of finches and the drill-hammer of a woodpecker. From where I sat, I could still hear the sounds of our estate through the streets; a lawnmower and a shout from a back garden. Other children playing. I hadn't walked far and yet, sitting there on the tree, I felt distanced. Removed. As I sat there, the fear began to subside. The longer I sat there, as the forest relaxed around me, the more at ease I became. The ants had never stopped working beneath my feet, but now other living creatures came into view. A red squirrel. The flash of a jay. A dragonfly. In my *Explorer's Journal* there was a spotter's list, but I didn't want to get it out of my bag in case I disturbed the scene; so I made a mental note of everything I had seen, all those things I had previously missed or scared into hiding.

I have no idea how long I sat there. To my ten-year-old self it felt like hours. The whole afternoon, at least. Perhaps even the whole day. In reality, I doubt it was that long. I'm not even sure my parents noticed I was gone. At dusk I stood up from where I had been sitting. I suppose I still had a choice at that moment. I could take the path further into the forest, to search for a place to build my makeshift tent. It would be easy, I could see as I looked around, to find the sticks and the stones to make it work. But I didn't have anything to eat. The banana was long gone. My packing list was incomplete.

I looked the other way. Back down the path, towards the wasteland and the rear gardens of our estate. Back towards home. It didn't take me long to decide. I went home. I was ten years old.

♦   ♦   ♦

My adventure was short, but I never forgot that afternoon, even if I could no longer remember what it was that had caused me to head off in the first place. By the time I returned to our garden and the house, carefully replacing the groundsheet in the garage and my money in the piggybank, something had changed. I had lost my fear of the forest.

I returned to the thick roots of that old tree many times in the years that followed. I would go alone, with a book, or with my music fed through headphones so as not to disturb the other creatures around me. I went there with friends, to build dens and, much later, to drink warm cans of beer or fizzy, sticky alcoholic fruit drinks. I went there with my parents and then, after my father died, my mother. After she passed away, I went there once more, walking out after the funeral and the wake held in a house that I knew I would never return to.

♦   ♦   ♦

I haven't been back. Not to the house or to the woods. And yet, in my mind I return to the forest often, awake and dreaming. I return and sit there for a while, resting on those thick roots of my old tree, and just listen.

# STORIES

The first tales of the forest that I learned came from my father. He would tell us the stories at bedtime, the tops of the trees visible across the garden from the bedroom window, but he preferred to tell them on location. It was one of his favourite things, I think, to take us out from the house on a weekend for a walk in the woods, using the stories of the forest as a means to distract us, so that we would forget our grumblings about aching feet or the television programmes that were going unwatched as we walked.

I don't know if he invented these stories, if he had heard or read them someplace else, or if it was a mixture of both. One thing that was consistent was his insistence that what he spoke was the truth, however fantastical the stories might seem. The world, he would say, has not always been like it is now. It hasn't always worked in the way that it does now, and it won't work this way forever. Anything is possible, in the past or in the future.

◆　◆　◆

His favourite characters, who he returned to time and again, were a tribe of short, fat creatures who had once called the forests around our town home, back when most people travelled overland by foot or, if they could afford it, by horse. These mischievous dwarves seemed to exist only to annoy passing travellers, by turning, for example, a puddle into ice at the height of summer so that someone would slip and fall, or by pinching a hole in a farmer's sack, so that by the time he reached the market one town over all the apples had escaped and rolled into the undergrowth by the edge of the track.

The dwarves, my father said, had magical powers that allowed them to set traps for vagabonds, moving the path on those who were lost so that it led, not out of the forest, but deeper in towards a swampy dead end. Most of their antics were playful and ultimately harmless, unless you happened to get stuck in the swamp or relied on the sales of your apples at the market to make a living, but one day their fun and games came to an abrupt end when our father told us the story of what finally happened to them.

Not far from our school, a cobblestone road led out from the town towards the next village over. It was lined with pollarded oaks, creating an avenue between the fields. This had once all been forest, my father said, and the road was laid to allow carriages to make the journey through the trees. Of course, carriages provided plenty of opportunities for the dwarves to get up to even more mischief, by startling the horses or loosening the nuts that held the wheels in place. But one day they rerouted the road once more, leading a passing druid down into the swamp. Perhaps they hadn't realised this was a man of magic, but he was certainly unimpressed with his robes getting dirtied by the muddy waters, and he cast a spell on the dwarves that left them frozen, for all time, as the oaks that lined the roadway. He froze them there, my father said, as a warning to all others of their kind not to get up to any similar tricks, and indeed, that appeared to be the end of those.

I remember standing in front of the oaks, running my hands over the rough bark as I tried to work out if the nobbles and knots were the features of the poor, frozen dwarves, thinking that the punishment seemed excessive compared to the crime. Even as a child, as my father finished the story, I couldn't help but think that the druid was guilty of a massive and ludicrous overreaction to what was, ultimately, just a bit of cheekiness on the part of the dwarves. The oaks, my father said, stood as a reminder of times we couldn't remember, and there were many such links to the past in the forest.

◆　◆　◆

One day we got in the car and drove a few miles south to where a forest trail led between huge boulders, glacial erratics transported from the far, frozen north many thousands of years before. They had been carried by enormous, continent-crossing glaciers, only to be left behind when the ice began to melt. That was, at least, what our teachers told us when they took us on a field trip into the forest. But my father had other ideas.

These boulders and the uneven, undulating ground upon which they rested, he said, were indeed from a very different time to our own. They dated back, he insisted, to the time of the giants, when most of the land was bare and the trees were just tiny saplings, crushed by the enormous feet of these creatures as they wandered the land. The boulders were the giants' weapons, used in fights between tribes that could flare up at any time, based upon a broken code of honour or perceived slight. In peacetime, the tribes would collect their boulders in one place – and here my father insisted that we would see remnants of these weapon stores if we ever took a trip to the mountains – with the intention that their piles would grow so big the other tribes wouldn't dare go into battle with them again.

It didn't work, and in my father's telling of the story the ultimate battle raged for decades, wiping out most of the giants and leaving the ground cratered and scarred, the battlefield strewn with their abandoned weaponry. Nobody won, as the battle ended not in victory or defeat but in exhaustion. The surviving giants retreated, and in their absence the forest could finally grow, swallowing the story with trees and brambles and ferns. But the stones remained, out of place and out of time, as a reminder of what came before.

◆  ◆  ◆

The forest can hold many stories, my father said, but it can also decide to reveal its secrets. And often there were enough clues to get you started, if you knew where to look.

# RESTORATION

In the grounds of a manor house, not far from where I grew up, there was a small graveyard that was the final resting place of the landowner and his wife. They had remained childless and had decided, long before they passed away, that the gardens and hunting grounds were going to be left to the people of the town, for eternity, in exchange for the maintenance and upkeep of their modest graveyard at the heart of the forest. Unfortunately, over the decades that followed, the people did not keep up their side of the bargain, and the little fenced-off plot of land was left, neglected and ignored, to become overgrown. It almost disappeared completely, and those walking the footpath, just metres from where the landowner and his wife lay, could do so with no knowledge of what might be found among the brambles and bushes that had swallowed the graveyard whole.

It was during my teenage years that the tiny graveyard was discovered, and the local newspaper began a campaign to raise some money to bring a little dignity back to the place, with new headstones, landscaping and a neat iron fence to mark the plot. They made the appeal to our collective guilt. After all, hadn't most of us, at some point or other, enjoyed the former gardens and hunting grounds of the manor house? Hadn't we walked its footpaths, pilfered firewood and collected blackberries? Hadn't we loaded up our baskets and plastic carrier bags with mushrooms, and filled our pockets with smooth, polished conkers?

The money was indeed raised, and workers employed to carry out the restoration of the graveyard, but before they did so, researchers came out from the city to investigate the site further, and in the course of their excavation of the fringes of the burial site they came upon a third grave a few metres from the two they already knew about. Within it they discovered the remains of a small child, and further analysis back in the city showed that the child had been buried there either around the same time as, or perhaps even a bit earlier than, the landowner and his wife. The discovery led to further investigations, of family, church and town records, searching for evidence of a child that until then nobody knew existed. But no evidence was found as to who it might have been.

The story of the child buried in the forest caused much debate in the local newspaper, as historians, both professional and amateur, sent in their theories to the letters page. My father would read them out over breakfast, and we would discuss which seemed the most plausible. Not that it really mattered, my father said. Not after all these years. It was a tragedy, regardless. Any child's death was a tragedy, whatever the reason might've been.

# THE GIRL IN THE BOX

The story began, as so many did, as whispers down the bottom of the school field. It was a story of another young person found buried in the forest, and it was one known to anyone growing up in our town or the surrounding villages. It was a story from nearby, but it was not our story. It belonged instead to a town a little further down the railway line, one that was just far enough away that none of us knew anyone from there, and it resonated not because of the mystery behind it, of not knowing how an anonymous child ended up buried in the woods, but because of the details that were only too well known and so gleefully spread.

The girl never had a name when the story was told, a fact that should have told us something but didn't. It began with her at a dance class, or a music lesson. Sometimes she was visiting friends. Whichever version of the story you heard, she then called her mother to say that she was on her way home. It was a short distance through the forest, and she was on her bicycle. It would only take ten minutes. But she never made it. Half an hour after she was supposed to return, her mum started walking the path through the forest. Somewhere along the way, she found her daughter's bicycle, abandoned by the side of the track, dumped in the ferns.

The police were called, search parties formed. Members of the fire brigade and the local Scouts gathered in a car park on the edge of the forest and were given photocopied maps with specific areas to cover. They fanned out, joined by the girl's parents and parents of her friends, her name echoing in the trees. It went on for days. Weeks. Sniffer dogs were deployed, as helicopters with state-of-the-art heat sensors hovered over the site where the bicycle was found. Nothing. And then one day someone was out for a walk, or a morning jog, and saw something suspicious. Flattened grass and the handle of a shovel, dumped in a bramble bush. Once again the police were called, and this time they found something. This time they found what they had been looking for.

There was no happy ending. The girl had been buried in a shallow grave, curled up in a wooden crate. The girl in the box. We told each other this story as a warning, to frighten our friends about what might happen if you wandered between the trees alone. After all, nobody had ever been charged with her murder, we whispered down the bottom of the school field. The person who had done this had never been caught…

Except. Except.

The story was true. Or at least a version of the story was true. It was famous even, making headlines in the national newspapers, spreading beyond the country's borders to make the bulletins in other places and in other languages. The girl's name had most certainly been known. But not to us, because the story of the real girl in the box had happened twenty years before we were born and in a town about as far from our home as it was possible to be without leaving the country. Another time, another place.

Yet the story had survived, carried on the breeze and between the trees, from the forests down there to the woods up here, passed on in playgrounds and on patches of wasteland at the edge of the forest. A cautionary tale. A warning to all. Wherever there were trees, and girls riding home on bicycles, the story echoed.

When I was about the same age as the girl in the box, my best friend lived on the other side of the woods. I no longer had the *Explorer's Journal*, but I still had the spotter's list, frayed and folded and stuffed into different jackets and scrawled on with so many different pens.

| | |
|---|---|
| Ferns | X |
| Beetle | X |
| Silver Birch | X |
| Red Admiral Butterfly | X |
| Woodpecker | X |
| Speckled Wood Butterfly | |
| Violet | X |
| Bumblebee | X |
| Ash Leaf | |
| Spider | X |
| Hedgehog | X |
| Deer | X |
| Squirrel | X |
| Bluebell | X |
| Owl | |
| Ladybird | X |
| Oak Leaf | X |
| Wild Boar | |
| Pine Cone | X |
| Orchid | X |

I never did spot them all.

# AT THE END OF THE TUNNEL

For a long time the party was only a rumour. An overhead conversation in the school corridor. A whisper in the lunch queue. Hints dropped in text messages by friends who knew as little as she did.

> *R U going?*
> *It's on the 14th!!!*
> *Will HE be there???*
> *Did he invite you yet?*
> *i heard friday…*

The kids who were organising it had to be careful, otherwise it would be stopped before it began. She had heard the previous parties had been legendary, and she knew, vaguely, some of the people involved. They were older than her in school, but one of them had promised to let her know as long as she didn't tell too many of her friends. That's what he said, and she agreed, willingly.

The location was well hidden, in a hollow beyond the railway lines. To reach it, you either took the footpath from behind the police station and into the woods, or you walked the shoulder of the road out of town for about a mile until you reached the turnoff. There was a ruined house up there, known to all the kids in the school. It was hard up against the railway tracks, roofless and filled with bushes, creepers and young trees, as well as all the remnants of the lives once lived there. Curls of faded wallpaper. A hairbrush on a windowsill. A cracked toilet filled with pine cones. There were plenty of tales about the house, stories that kept people away and off the footpath that ran past it and through the dark, dripping tunnel beneath the railway that led deeper into the forest.

The path was so unused that the other side of the tunnel had become overgrown, but when she reached it, she could see exactly where she was supposed to go. A flattened trail through the long grass led her between tall pines to where the ground lifted up. Breathing heavily, she climbed the side of the low, steep hill and then dropped down the other side into the bottom of what was a narrow, dry valley, scoured out of the land many thousands of years before. Pines grew all around, on the ridge and the slopes, but the valley floor was clear. It was the perfect hiding place. She only heard the music when she first crested the hill and the party was already in sight. As long as everyone had played by the rules, nobody would disturb them.

◆  ◆  ◆

He seemed pleased to see her, and even more pleased that she hadn't invited any of her friends. There had been texts flying back and forth all day, the rumours intensifying, but she had kept quiet and then, when the direct question came and silence was no longer an option, she lied. Did she want to come with them to the lake, as they did every Friday evening that summer? No, she wrote. She had to help her mum with something. It was a pain. Unfair. But it couldn't be helped.

Someone pressed a beer into her hand. The air around her a drifting cloud of smoke; joints and cigarettes. A jam jar filled with water was passed between the smokers as they took a final drag. The fire warning was high that summer and they had to be careful.

She sat down next to him on a fallen tree trunk and sipped her beer, listening to the conversation and the music. She did not trust herself yet to join in, although everyone had been friendly. Some were already dancing, but most were sitting around. She knew her friends would be disappointed in her when they found out, but she also felt they would be disappointed if they could see what they were missing. They'd all heard so much about these forest parties, hidden from view, from the parents and the police. But this was nothing particularly special. What was *special*, she thought, dropping her chin to her chest so that no one could see her smile, was that she was there, and her friends were not. That she had been *invited*. The rest would take care of itself.

◆  ◆  ◆

It must have been later. High summer and dark now, a few stars visible through the clearing in the canopy above her head. Someone had fixed transparent coloured paper to heavy industrial torches, which shone their reds, blues, yellows and greens against the slender trunks of the pines all around them. The music was louder than before, as if darkness offered a greater protection. More people were dancing, a mass of bodies, of limbs, moving right in front of her. She stayed where she was, feeling the alcohol, moving to the music but not ready to join them.

He was sitting next to her. He told her why they held their parties in the forest. It gave them privacy, yes. But it was more than that. He asked her if she had ever been in the forest at night. If she had ever heard the forest at night. She told him that she hadn't, and then she laughed, feeling the alcohol a little more, and said that all she could see were the lights and the limbs, and all she could hear was the thump of the music.

He stood up and pulled her to her feet. Still holding her hand, he led her away from the party, down the valley and into the darkness.

They had to wait a moment, he said, once they had walked about forty paces from the clearing. Their eyes would get used to it. The pines were spread out there, and there was a full moon. It didn't take long for their eyes to adjust and the trees to appear, along with ghostly ferns and dark shapes in the distance that she prayed would not move. They walked on, further along the valley, and she couldn't hear the music now, just the movement of the trees and a goods train rattling along the tracks in the distance.

People were scared of the forest, he said, but not him and his friends. That's why they had made it their place. Who was going to step into the darkness of that tunnel and go deep into the forest to look for them? As long as they cleared all traces and didn't start any fires, it could belong to them. It was all theirs. Freedom.

She felt bark through her thin T-shirt, rough against her back. Fingers intertwined. Lips. The kiss was a shock, even though she knew it was coming. Had wanted it to come. She lifted her hand to his face. Rough, unshaven. She felt his hands on her waist. On cotton, then skin. Lines traced. Up. Across. Down. There. There.

No. Not yet.

The hand moved. A gentle voice, asking a soft question. Fingers still there. Moving back. Still moving. Still touching.

Not yet. I'm sorry.

Not yet.

It was okay. She apologised again. He forgave her. She liked him even more then, and wondered if she'd made a mistake. It would take her a long, long time before she began to question why she felt she had to apologise. They walked back down the valley towards the party, to the music. He began to dance. She wanted to go home but she took another beer. Sat back down on the fallen tree trunk. It was all normal. It was all cool.

◆　◆　◆

She left alone, as the sun came up. The party site slowly came into view, and she could see people sleeping, leaves piled up around them, along with bottles and cans and items of discarded clothing. Others continued to dance, slower now, the music lower, trance-like. With the sun came the cold, a morning chill, and she shivered in her T-shirt as she stood. There was no sign of him.

She followed the beaten path through the long grass, down the tunnel and past the ruined house. She crossed the road and took the forest path back into town, not wanting to leave the sanctuary of the woods just yet. What would the early morning driver think, to see her walking down the side of the road? It felt safer in the forest. As she got closer to town, her phone received a signal once more, for the first time since the previous evening.

*It was tonight, right?*
*you can tell me.*
*What happened?*
*Did you…*

She pressed delete, the little rubber buttons cold to her fingertips. There would be time for a post-mortem on Monday morning. She still had time to get the story straight.

♦ ♦ ♦

At the end of August, a message was sprayed onto the red-brick walls of the tunnel beneath the railway tracks. SUMMER CLUB 2001. A series of letters. DK. F-LJ. ST. AP. DL… There were about thirty sets of initials in all, and the first time she saw it she could put a name to most of them. They had got together at their hollow in the forest a final time, in the last weeks before many of them left the town and their childhood behind them. There had been fewer rumours about that final party. It was the holidays. For most of them, school was over. The world was waiting. The final party. She wasn't invited.

♦ ♦ ♦

About fourteen years later she was back in the town, collecting a piece of paper from the council offices, and decided to go for a walk. She followed the road out of town until she reached the turnoff, then crossed the small field that led to the railway embankment, the ruined house and the tunnel beneath the tracks. It had been used as a fly-tipping spot, the contents of what looked like a garage dumped on the edge of the path. Petrol cans and oil canisters. A set of tyres and a rusted toolkit. A calendar, twelve years old, and rags, so many rags, their colours dulled and stained with water and oil and grease.

The path through the tunnel and into the forest was now part of a hiking route, with signs hammered into the soft ground and marked on trees to help people find their way. The tunnel was still damp, the water dripping from the ceiling even in the midst of a long, long heatwave. The paint was still visible on the wall, faded slightly, but it was still possible to read, to make out the letters. Some of the names had been lost, but others remained clear as if they were standing in front of me, unchanged in a decade and a half.

She stood in the half-light of the tunnel, the ground muddy underfoot. She put my fingers to the wall, touching the old paint. She remembered.

# HERMITAGE

For three summers a man lived in the woods, not far from the mobile phone mast that had been erected on the highest hill in the area. His encampment was substantial and not particularly well hidden, made up of a frame tent plus two smaller canvas structures, one on either side, and a set of Tibetan prayer flags hung between them. Although it was clearly forbidden to live like this in the forest, he was left alone by the authorities and was even allowed to leave his rubbish by the side of the service track that led to the mobile phone mast, and have it collected by the lorries travelling out from town to the more remote farms further along the forest road.

An artist, some said. A recluse. He was on some kind of spiritual retreat. A writer. A researcher. A tramp. A bum. A refugee.

He would come into town almost daily, and for all the stories that went around about him, nobody asked him any difficult questions. He went swimming at the pool, taking long showers both before and after. He picked up his mail, including numerous parcels, from the post office. And he sat most afternoons in the cafe, where he drank cups of black coffee and charged his phone.

◆　◆　◆

The first summer he was the subject of much curiosity in town. The police were disinclined to get involved; most people came to the conclusion that he had permission to be up there. When September came, and the leaves began to turn, he was spotted at the train station. His encampment was secured but not removed, covered with thick, heavy tarpaulins pegged into the ground. It might have been expected that someone would mess with his belongings over the long winter, but they never did, and when he returned the following May everything was exactly as he'd left it.

The second summer, people stopped wondering. Every place had its characters, the town collectively reasoned, and every place had its eccentrics. People simply got used to them. By the third summer he would be greeted with a nod or a wave, maybe even a smile on his walks into town. Someone from the post office began dropping his letters and parcels off at the cafe so he didn't have to walk all the way to the other end of town to get them, and the librarian shyly approached him one afternoon and said he could take books out if he liked, even if – and here she coughed a little nervously – he didn't have a permanent address.

One weekend the librarian read of a book in the newspaper that she ordered as soon as she got into work on Monday morning.

*The forest is natural space*, the librarian read, *but it is also a transgressive space. It is a place beyond the normal structures of society. It is a place of illicit activity; of forbidden sex; of true freedom. It can be this because it is older than anything of our creation. We cannot make rules for a place we do not properly understand. Where we do not and cannot possibly know all of its secrets. It is the place where Barbarians dwell; where your civilisation will come to harm should you try and tame it. It is the Holy Wilderness. It doesn't care for your rules. It will be here longer than anything you might build in its place, and it is just waiting to return as soon as what you have replaced it with starts to crumble. No human empire has ever held as much territory as the forest. And be sure of one thing: it will reclaim that lost territory. It will take it back...*

When it arrived, the librarian left the book where she thought he would find it, face up on the table where she gathered her most favoured selections, but he never picked it up.

♦   ♦   ♦

They were used to him in town by that third summer, and there were some who looked upon him with what can only be described as envy. Of how he lived his life. Of his summers in the forest. Of how he somehow made it work, beyond the usual limits and limitations. Yes, there was a part of some of them that wished, if only for a moment, that they could live like that too. Even if they had no knowledge of how and where he spent the winter.

That September he shut up his camp as he had the previous two autumns and made his way down the hill on the short walk to the railway station. The following spring, those who'd had more to do with him, such as the cafe owner, the librarian and the women who worked the supermarket checkouts, began to idly wonder when he would return. They found they were looking forward to seeing him again, to the routines of this man from the forest who had come to symbolise the arrival of summer.

But the fourth summer, he did not return. May came, then June. July and August. The encampment remained shrouded in its heavy tarpaulin. By the end of the summer the first tent pegs had been pulled out. The old frame tent was exposed. The door unzipped and left open, and things taken out. When autumn came, the leaves turned and fell, the encampment was left open to the elements. In the winter, snow piled high where he once slept, where he once cooked, and where he once read his library books.

The following spring the council sent a truck and two men up the forest road and down the service track. Wearing overalls and heavy gloves, they pulled out what remained of the encampment from the tangle of bushes that had begun to swallow it, and lifted it into the back of the truck. When they were finished there was no sign of the man who had lived there for three summers, except for an odd flattening of the forest floor where the encampment had once been. Whatever it was – art performance, writer's retreat, research project or mid-life crisis – it was now over. The council workers made sure no traces were left, and it wouldn't be long before even the memories of his presence began to fade, questioned and unsure.

# A WOODEN HOUSE

He had always dreamed of a wooden house, one which, he said, would have that smell. And he didn't need to describe it, because everyone he told his dream to knew what smell he was talking about. After the divorce, once the apartment was sold, he moved out of the city and used his half of the proceeds to have a wooden house built, right on the edge of a town, on a plot of land cleared from the forest. The town was new to me, although like an unfamiliar port on a familiar sea, the forest that stretched out from where his house rose from the muddy ground was the same as the one I had explored in my childhood, a few dozen miles away to the east.

During the construction phase we lived in a small flat in the basement of one of our future neighbours. They had converted the space beneath the ground floor for an elderly parent who never made it, and now they supplemented their income by renting it to a mix of hikers and cyclists out from the city for a few days, and construction workers from across the border who earned their money on building sites and renovation projects away from home for a few weeks or months at a time. We lived in the flat for about six months. I got to know the new town and he fretted over each of the many decisions necessary when building a house from scratch, and even though I was to live in it, it was an unspoken agreement between us that this was *his* house and *his* project, and so I offered an opinion only when he asked for it.

When the house was almost complete, just before the men in harnesses arrived in their van to hang from the rafters and fix the roof tiles, a small fir tree was attached to the highest point. We shared bottles of fizzy wine and beer laid out on a camping table between the concrete mixer and a portable toilet that stood in the place where, one day, guests would be welcomed onto a wooden terrace for drinks. This topping out ceremony was important, he said, because if you built a house out of wood, out of the forest itself, you had to show the tree spirits thanks and that they still had a place to live. It was an old custom, he explained, from a belief system that had no adherents except for this one tradition among the building trade, who continued to maintain it even when constructing huge tower blocks of concrete, steel and glass. If the tree spirits were calm, he continued, filling our plastic cups once more, then it would be a happy house. We drank to that.

◆  ◆  ◆

A few weeks later, with the house almost complete, a gardener came to talk about the space behind, where the plot of land ran down towards the simple wire fence that marked the edge of the property. Beyond it was a pine plantation, slender trees with soft grass at their base, and the telltale sign of turned-over earth that spoke of night-time foraging by wild boars. There were three trees standing within the garden itself. Did he, the gardener asked, want them removed? The answer was no. He liked the idea that the forest came into the garden. If it wasn't for the boars, he continued, he would have the fence removed.

◆ ◆ ◆

During the period of my life that I lived in that house, I would often sit at the open window of what we called the guest room but which was, in fact, the dumping ground for what would normally have ended up in the basement or loft. The house had neither. I would sit by the window on an old office chair I had brought from my last apartment, next to boxes of what were mostly my books, never to be unpacked, and I would listen. Sometimes I heard owls. A rustle by the fence. Once, and only once, the howl of what I was sure was a wolf. In the daytime, the pine plantation beyond the garden fence seemed dead, devoid of life. Perhaps a solitary jay or a lonely woodpecker, but for the most part, nothing. At night, though, listening from above, I could sense the life of the forest. I could feel the movement in the darkness, of the boar and the deer, the badgers and the hedgehogs. Somewhere, out there, the wolves wandered the edge of their territory, ever alert, able to detect my presence up at the window from many miles away.

He never went into the forest. He didn't need to. He had surrounded himself with it in the house, with its wooden walls and wooden ceilings, the work surfaces and bookshelves, kitchen tables and chairs, the high stools by the breakfast bar. It wasn't unusual. That is to say, he wasn't unusual. Don't we all like wood? Don't we all trust wood, somehow, more than any other material? Don't we instinctively feel that a wooden toy is better, more educational, somehow, more wholesome, than anything made out of plastic? A wooden table, he once said, connects us to the past, to our ancestors and our traditions. There had been a time, for a few decades in the middle of the last century, where we had embraced the manmade. Formica. Plastic. Glass. But then, he continued, we retreated. We pulled up our carpets to expose the floorboards, stripping doors and investing in brand new kitchens designed and made out of wood. Designed to look old, to connect us to some idea of the past. We returned to the woods.

I did not live in that wooden house for very long. It marked the end point for many things, and the start of my own retreat, for a while, from the forest. Later, in the city, I would also sit at an open window, listening to the cars and the conversation from the street below. In moments of calm, when the city was stilled for a second or two, I would hear the rustle of leaves as the trees that lined the pavement blew in the wind and I was taken back to the window of the guest room or the forest paths of my childhood. There was life there, in the city. A red squirrel that came up onto my balcony. A family of foxes, living by the railway tracks. Grey herons in the stream and goshawks in the park. There was more life there, a neighbour once said to me, than in whole swathes of the countryside. I found it hard to believe but it was true. Modern farming was to blame.

But still, as much as I felt a sense of relief on moving to the city, a feeling of new possibilities that were not to be found in however many towns and villages I tried on the edge of the forest, I did miss it. I missed its presence at the bottom of the garden. Listening for owls. Listening for wolves. I didn't miss anything else about the wooden house, but I did miss that.

# WOLVES

When I was a child there were no wolves in the forest. They existed only in fairy tales and history books; real creatures that had been made mythical by our ancestors hundreds of years before. Once they were gone, hunted to the tops of the very highest mountains and the bottoms of the very deepest valleys, they could be turned into anything we liked. Now that they were mythical creatures in our corner of the planet, they could become symbols for all manner of fantasies and yearnings, symbols of evil and witchcraft, of temptation and threat. A pair of eyes, glowing in the shadows. A howl at the moon. My, Grandma, what big teeth you have!

In their absence, their legend increased. In distant lands, far from the trappers and hunters, they managed to survive, as real as they had ever been. But in the forests of my childhood, they were legend, as mythical as unicorns or dragons.

◆ ◆ ◆

At some point between my childhood explorations of the forest and moving into the wooden house, the wolf returned. The territory of our local pack stretched from the forest of my childhood to the woods at the edge of the unfamiliar town I found myself in. They patrolled beneath the trees, using motorways and railway lines, bicycle paths and foresters' tracks to navigate and demarcate. They kept themselves to themselves. All who walked in those woods knew they were there, but never expected to meet them. I was more scared of coming between a boar and her young than any furred figure from a childhood story.

Nevertheless, within the town and around, people began to panic. Videos were shared over the internet, of mutilated livestock and muddy fields of scattered feathers. Hunters, high in their wooden chairs, their pulpits from which they issued their death sentences, saw deadly competition. Parents feared for their children. Centuries of stories echoed in the imagination. Hysteria rising. As if unicorns were real. As if dragons had been born.

◆ ◆ ◆

Soon, there was blood. A female wolf was found, mutilated and dumped in the pond of a village about two miles from our town. It was not so much her death that was shocking but the frenzy of the killing. She had been caught, tortured, and her life finally ended, presumably by people who lived in or near the village. Who loved their livestock. Loved their children. Loved their dogs. Deep fears had turned into bloodlust and violence.

I was glad the wolves were back, but I was scared for them. I wanted to tell them that maybe they should have stayed where they were, in the high mountains and the remote places, far from those who would do them harm. I wanted to tell them that down here, in our forest, there were people who were out to get them. The stories had always got things the wrong way round. The threat wasn't the wolf, disguised or otherwise. It was Grandma, holding a rifle.

# GLOAMING

The forest at dusk. You can feel the ground beneath your feet change as you step from the concrete-slab pavement and onto the soft footpath leading away through the trees. It has been raining for days, flooding gutters and gardens, soaking the soil. There were moments, as you sat at the window with the water hammering at the glass and the wind whipping branches from the trees, when it felt as if it would never end. That the rain would keep falling and falling until the waters rose and washed everything away. Sitting at the window, the darkness of the house at your back, it did not seem like the worst thing that could happen.

But it stopped. Of course it did. And for an hour or so the sun came through to bathe everything in a soft orange light and it felt like hope, if only until it dipped behind the horizon. And here you are, standing on the path at the edge of the forest, waiting for your eyes to adjust to the half-light. All those days in the house, stuck behind glass, have brought you to this. The need to walk. The need to breathe. The need to escape. It's okay, he said. He understood. But you're not sure that he does.

In this light the forest is at its most suggestive. Every shadow seems to move. Every fallen tree or crooked branch the limb of some unknown creature. Normally you like to step off the path, to move through the trees, imagining you are the only person to have taken that particular route through the forest in living memory, but right now you stick to the muddy trail like your father instructed you to do when you were young and alone in the woods. Follow the footprints of those who have gone before you. Men and dogs. Women and deer. Children, wild boar and wolves.

What else lives here, among these trees? You recall the stories, your father's gentle voice. There was no need to shout in the forest, he said, as he explained all the living beings that surrounded you. Just because we've never seen them, he said, doesn't mean they're not here. After all, what happens to things when we discover them? The hunters' pulpits were evidence enough of that. Why would you show yourself, if to show yourself was to issue your own death sentence? You can still see the certainty in his eyes when he delivered those words. The surety of his step as he walked away down the path, truth told. He would have liked it that the wolves have returned.

Your eyes have adjusted now but you still walk carefully. Tree roots cross the path, waiting to trip you. Branches drop down to head height, like fingers reaching out to poke at the eyes. Are you not scared? You can still hear his voice, half an hour ago in the kitchen, as you pulled on your boots, the last of the sun shining in through the window. He was sitting at the table in front of his laptop, the code for Do Not Disturb, yet it was he who wanted to start the conversation. No, you were not scared. What was there to be scared of? Worse things happened behind walls and doors than between the trees. That was simply a fact.

The path opens out here, into a clearing where there is a picnic table for hikers and a signpost detailing the options, with destinations and distances, and the estimated time it will take to get there. You sit down on the bench by the table, the forest around you and the stars emerging above the clearing, and you wait for the message that must surely come. If not tonight, then when?

*The forest rustled gently,*
*So starry was the night.*
*And my soul spread out its wings so wide,*
*To fly through these silent lands,*
*As if to fly home.*

How well do you remember the words? The book was one of the first presents he gave you. Hardcover, with an expensive binding. An old-fashioned typescript and heavy paper. It was a serious present, one to welcome you to the house. A symbol of what you meant to him. For a long time, it sat by your side of the bed. To show him that you appreciated it, that you wanted to keep his gift close, though you'd read many of those poems at school; heard them, and read them out loud, and you had even taken them to the places they were supposed to be about. Tried to find their presence there. But you never did, and so the poems left you cold. You could not connect. This was not how you felt, and so the book stayed on the bedside table, unopened and unread.

Why didn't you tell him?

You lose track of how long you sit there in the clearing. Streaky clouds cross the sky, blocking some of the stars, darkening the night. You have no way to tell the time. No way of being contacted. Your phone sits on the kitchen counter, by the back door. If he has tried to call you, he will have found it by now. You can see him, holding both phones, one in each hand. Reading his own name. Seeing yours. Cursing yours, your forgetfulness, your *irresponsibility*. You can hear him forming the syllables, spitting them out. But he shouldn't worry. You'll be home soon. The last thing you'd want to do is worry him. Practise the words. It would be a distraction. You know that. Nothing can be allowed to get in the way.

Do Not Disturb.

# TWO

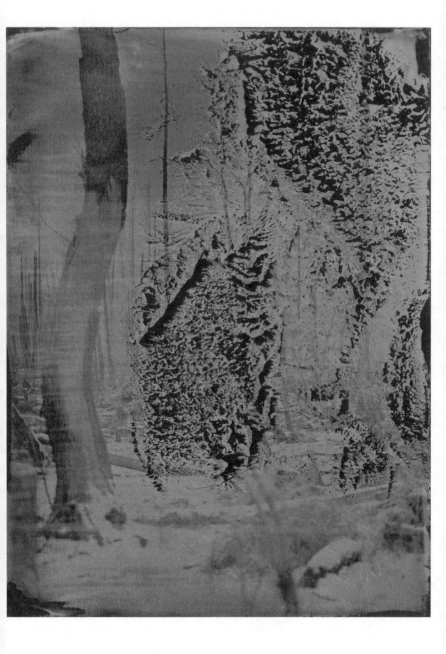

# BETWEEN THE VILLAGES

Tarmac becomes cobblestones becomes sandy soil as the old road leads out of the village towards the forest. It used to be the main route between the villages, creating a chain that linked them all to the town and the market square, but it is a long time since anyone used these old ways for trade or transport. The main road cuts through the forest to the south. The railway cuts across the fields to the north. The track is now the preserve of the horse-riders and cyclists, and those who travel by foot, just as in earlier times.

At different points along the trail, works of art have been placed, sharing space with the pines and silver birches, the oaks and the beeches. These artworks were installed to bring more people to the old way, a tourist attraction as well as a commentary on history and the natural environment. As people move between them, locals or visitors, they can learn some of the stories of this place and this landscape. A pack of fake wolves. A doorway to nowhere, speaking to the villages long-abandoned to nature. A set of metal crates, designed to say… what? Caged animals, transported from shed to slaughterhouse? Organic boxes, to sell to the urban middle classes? Or the way the dice falls. How life changes.

People move on. Others take their place. Some come back.

My neighbour rides his bike between the villages daily, ever since they closed the pub at the end of the street. The landlord was retiring and there was no one around to take it on, and the handful of regular drinkers that called it home. Now, for his beer and whisky, his conversation and silent companionship, my neighbour has to ride the old way through the woods, following the line of fruit trees where we all go to gather damsons and apples when the time is right, past the artwork and across the fields. Tarmac and cobblestone. Sand to trip his tyres. There is always at least one stretch where he has to climb down from his bike to give it a push.

He chooses this way rather than the main road because the road is too busy, choked with cars and farm vehicles and lorries cutting between the motorways. They shake the village houses as they pass, an articulated earthquake at regular intervals throughout the day. When he takes the track, he needs about forty minutes to ride between the villages and, although sometimes he might meet someone along the way, usually he has the journey all to himself.

He doesn't make the trip to the pub on weekends. If he did he would meet more people, walkers especially, out from the towns and the city to hike the trail between the railway stations, ticking off the different works of art as they go. Because my neighbour is elderly, and still wears his old work boots all year round, when they see him tending his garden or sitting on the chair he keeps by the front step of his cottage they look upon him as if he is one of the exhibits, a bit of local colour; a genuine country dweller.

What they don't know is that he is from the city himself, that he moved out here all those years ago to work in the brewery, five and a half shifts a week. It was a difficult time, he once told me, leaving his life behind. For a while he would return to the city on his days off, visiting family and friends. He found life out here so dull and strange, and it was a feeling that stayed with him for so long that he didn't notice it gradually receding, until one day it was gone and he realised he was here to stay. Until that point, he couldn't have imagined it.

How the dice fall.

But I know how he feels. This has always been a land of exiles, a landscape of settlers. A thousand years ago they came from the west, brought here because their religion fit better for the rulers than that of the local population, and boasting the right skills to make the most of this sandy soil. Later it was the refugees, people fleeing war and economic hardship, and those who moved out from the city to find work, in a reversal of what had gone before. Later came the hippies and the back-to-the-land dreamers, and later still even more who came not through choice but necessity, brought here by bus and train, sleeping five to a room in an old factory dormitory on the edge of town, fleeing more modern wars.

The pub in our village has closed. The brewery where my neighbour worked for thirty years has long been abandoned. Now the beer is brought to the pub at the end of the track by lorry, made far away in an industrial park on the edge of the city, and the warehouse where my neighbour spent his days slowly crumbles, the roof open to the elements as saplings grow from the brickwork. Still, my neighbour says, you can't fault the beer nowadays. You know what you're going to get, which is different to in his day. It wasn't their fault, of course. You can only work with the ingredients you are given. You can only work with what you've got.

The weekend walkers who stop in the village square and look at the estate agent's listings in the window of the bank – open two hours a day, Monday to Thursday – wonder what it would be like to live out here with us; they like to think that the countryside is fixed. That while their neighbourhoods shift on uneasy foundations, out here things tend to stay the same, frozen in place. It is a comforting thought, but it has never been true. A thousand years of comings and goings. Towns with names born in long forgotten languages. Villages abandoned and swallowed by the forest. Traces of religions that no longer have any followers…

My neighbour rides his bike to the pub. He has lived through some of these changes in the years since he has moved out from the city, as I have lived them in the time since I returned. He sits at his usual table in the corner of the pub and reads the newspaper headlines. Old businesses fade into memory, as new initiatives are launched with regional funding, buzzwords and hope. Bands of old timers from a country that no longer exists gather together to rehearse for one final show. Beetles that were once rare now ravage the forest, alongside fires that burn hotter and more often than they ever did before. A new motorway bridge is built to help wild animals safely reach the other side. He sees the changes on every ride between the villages. Trees are felled. Another part of the brewery crumbles. The wolves return. Only the path stays the same. The only certainty is that at some point he'll have to get off and push.

# I READ THE NEWS TODAY, OH BOY...

At his table in the corner of the pub, he slowly turns the pages:

*Escaped water buffalo shuts the motorway for more than an hour.*

*Bridge collapse. More barriers for walkers and cyclists as council admits financial difficulties.*

*Fridays for Future: Local school children plant trees in response to climate crisis.*

*After a record year for forest fires: what next?*

*Wild boar destroys mayor's prize-winning garden in midnight rampage.*

*Lost mushroom forager found safe and well after twelve hours in the forest.*

*Farmer disorderly: drunk in charge of a tractor.*

*Fly-tipping epidemic. Asbestos ceiling panels, oil drums and carpet rolls just some of the rubbish found in the woods.*

*Record dry spell: forest on the verge of collapse following drought, storms and plague of bark beetles.*

*Wolf torture case begins.*

*A third of the forest in danger: how can we stop the forest death?*

Another turn of the page. At the stadium on the edge of town, his team played out a goalless draw. The game this weekend has been cancelled. Referee strike.

*Forest run – football team join charity jog after derby called off. All money raised to be donated to the local fire station.*

It's been a busy summer.

# TAKE ME TO CHURCH

The high heath where I live was formed by the Ice Age, a lumpy terrain where water is usually only found deep below the surface. Here, our valleys are dry, created as glacial drainage channels that, over the centuries, became the easiest route for travellers moving through the forest, from farm to farm and village to village. Over time the dry valleys became footpaths, named for those who used them. The pastor's way, linking one village church to the next. The brewer's way, wide enough to roll barrels through the woods. The paths cross in the middle of the forest, where the trees have thinned a little and in the summer there is a beautiful wildflower meadow. It always seems to me like the perfect place to rest, for a spot of holy refreshment as the pastor and the brewery boys make an unscheduled stop on their journeys through the trees.

I use these paths on my regular walks from home, a figure-of-eight route that starts where the gravel track from the main road meets the edge of the forest. I enter having hugged its fringe for a while, between the trees and a field where, in the summertime, corn grows high above my head. Once I've stepped off the track, I find myself in a huge, cavernous space beneath the canopy. This is beech forest here, the remnants of those that once filled a continent, and these beautiful trees stand tall and proud, like pillars in a cathedral holding up a vaulted roof.

Today, a light rain has started to fall as I make my way between the beech trees. I'm well protected here, from the rain and the outside world. It is why I keep coming back. Why I make this same walk, two or three times a week. The wind moves the upper branches and shakes moisture down from the canopy, but on the ground it is still. Two giant trees were felled in a recent storm, their roots weakened by the long dry summer. I take a break by resting on one, contemplating their loss, imagining the violence of the moment, the rupture of the dry soil and the creaking fall to earth.

The forest is damp, with a mulchy smell you can almost touch. It's the time of year when mushroom hunters are out in force, and I can hear voices from further down a path I often have all to myself. They come to the forest for what it can give them, in the same way I do, only I lack their expertise in what they can and can't pick, the mushrooms that will fill their bellies or poison their family. I've lived most of my life within sight of a forest and yet I've never trusted my knowledge. I know that I'm not alone. The mushroom foragers are in the minority, even out here. The rest of us go to the supermarket.

It shouldn't be a surprise. Outside of mushroom season, if I meet someone along the pastor's way or the brewer's way, at the fallen beech trees or the wildflower meadow, it is likely as not that they have come from elsewhere. I have the feeling that many in our village live alongside the forest but rarely go there, happy that it exists but happier in their gardens, with clear skies above their heads. We spent generations leaving the forest. Clearing the spaces on which we could grow and build, from farms to great cities.

We left the trees behind, abandoned the shadows and all who lived among them, exchanging the darkness for lightness and space.

I think of the stories my father used to tell me. The stories of the playground. The stories passed down over generations, written in books and turned into technicolour films. I think of the lonely soldier in front of a wall of trees. The darkness he is about to enter. Who believes these stories? Most of us, I think. They keep us out of the forest, away from the woods and what might happen in the shadows, in the darkness between the trees and beneath the canopy. Two children go off into the woods, a trail of breadcrumbs behind them. A sculpture made of branches, left in a clearing by an anonymous artist, gives us the shivers. Enter the forest at the start of a film and you're unlikely to come back out again. The stories are all designed to make sure we do not turn our backs on civilisation. That we stay close. That we obey the rules.

It is why I love the mushroom foragers, however grumpy they might be, concerned that I might be a rival for their favoured spot. We have a secret connection, the foragers and I, one that we share with all we pass on the path. In the forest, there's nothing to buy. No transaction to take place. The forest gives, but expects nothing in return. No wonder it is not trusted.

# THE FOREST AND THE CITY

The forest is waiting. The map tells you everything you need to know. Around the edge of the city it fills the space, a green expanse just beyond the dotted line. Some would tell you that it has been pushed out over the decades, and old maps collected in a stack at the library would agree. With every new building and car park, housing estate and school, road and railway line, the forest is in retreat. Look at the map today and it seems more like an advancing army, circling the walls, ready to lay siege.

It doesn't need to. The dotted line, the virtual walls that mark the divide, have already been breached. Green fingers reach in towards the city centre, following the routes of rivers and streams, circling the lakes and pushing on between the expanses of grey and yellow and dull pink that mark the industrial estates, retail zones and residential neighbourhoods that only make sense on the map, coloured in by someone desperately trying to find order in the urban chaos. What do they make of the forest, reaching in? The green lines are transit routes, with tarmac paths for cycling commuters, but others make use of them too. Boars come to savage back gardens. Pine martens strip out the brake lines of parked cars. Raccoons rifle through the bins.

When I lived in the city, I knew a woman who drew maps and sold them from a stall down by the museum. The map imagined the city never existed. No grey and yellow zones.

No dull pinks. Only rivers and streams, lakes and marshland. And lots and lots of green. I bought a print from her stall and took it to a shop to be framed. It hung on the wall above my kitchen table, next to the window with a view across the rooftops and the clutter of chimneys, aerials and mobile-phone masts high above the streets that had been deleted from the map. It was wishful thinking, her beautiful creation. The forest is waiting. It is ready to reclaim its lost territory. But it won't be the same. It can't be.

# FOREST DEATH / WALDSTERBEN

From where I stand, it feels as if the forest has been ripped out, wrenched from the soil by a giant hand, as easily as a clump of weeds pulled from the flower bed. At one end, a tractor works to clear the debris left behind. Remnants of trunks, hacked at and sawn off. Tangled roots and shredded bushes. Patches of sawdust, improbably clean. Everything else is muddy. It has been raining for days, softening the ground, the track that once led between the trees widened to twice or even three times its normal size to accommodate the unimaginable machines that have created this scene, churning the ground and leaving their giant treads imprinted on the earth.

At the edge of the empty space, of this cleared patch of forest, black boxes have been set up in front of the trees that still stand in the background. They are there to catch the bark beetles, who have been on the rampage after a run of dry summers, leaving behind the skeletons of once healthy trees, pockmarked with the entranceways to the tiny tunnels that have brought them down. Mild winters have allowed the beetle population to explode, breeding four generations in a year rather than one or two. It takes a healthy tree only four weeks to die, once the beetles have begun to lay their eggs inside.

Mild winters help the beetles flourish and during the hot summer the forest burns. Fires start ever earlier in the year and burn longer and more fiercely than any of us can remember. Whole swathes are lost to the flames as the smoke blocks out the sun and the sky glows red. Do we need any more warning than this, I think, as I hear the siren sound at the fire station in the centre of the village?

It seems that we do. And even when the fires don't come, or are extinguished through skill and a bit of luck before they can take hold, the dry ground struggles to keep everything upright. My beech trees were felled in a storm. They aren't the only ones that lie like fallen giants on the forest floor.

The loss is measured in football pitches, in numbers that we can understand but still can't quite comprehend. 250,000 in one year. We count the cost of reversing the loss in millions. Solutions come from all sides: diversify the forest; too many monocultures; too many single-species plantations. Introduce new trees, better suited to this warming world. Create more mixed forests, of broad-leaved native species. More wasps. More bees. It's time to get serious before it's too late. It's probably too late.

The debate rages. There are no answers. There are too many answers. Are we even asking the right questions?

The forest is waiting.

# RESURREXIT

In these times, the forest gives up some of its secrets. The boy was riding home from school when he saw smoke drifting across the bike path. Later, when he thought about all that was to follow, when he wrote his story down, he tried to remember why he had ridden that way rather than following the main road. It was because it was hot, he remembered. It had been hot for weeks. In school they worked with the windows wide open, even though the air outside was warmer than the air within. At home he had taken to sleeping in the basement, surrounded by the cool earth that pressed up against the crumbling walls. And on his ride home he had taken to using the forest path, riding beneath the trees that offered at least some protection from the relentless sun.

Protection, he wrote. That was what the forest meant to him. Some of his friends were scared of the woods, fed as children on a diet of fairy tales and horror stories, but he didn't feel like they did. Since he was small, his father had taken him for long walks. There was nothing to be scared of. If you wanted to, you could live forever on what the forest offered up. His father would list the foundations for survival, counting them off on his fingers. Water. Food. Shelter. The forest offered them all. You could live forever in the woods and need for nothing. Thinking about it later, forcing himself to remember, he could still hear the wistful tone in his father's voice.

◆　◆　◆

He smelled the smoke before he saw it. It was a smell out of time, of burning birch and fir, a smell that triggered memories not of summer but of late autumn, when the stoves of the village were stoked for the first time. When he saw the smoke drifting across the path he stopped and looked in through the trees. Small flames made a lot of smoke. He could hear the crackle of dry branches and the pop of pine cones exploding. Beyond the flames was the motorway with its cars, buses and lorries, all passing by. On the other side of the bike path, more forest. Stretching away to the south, the west and the east, surrounding villages and small hamlets. Very little water on the surface.

He called the emergency services. The woman on the end of the line told him to stay calm, although he wasn't panicking. The flames were still low. He used the map function to find his exact location, reading the string of numbers out. The woman thanked him and told him once more to stay calm. To ride home and not worry about it. The fire brigade were on their way.

◆　◆　◆

Throughout the afternoon and into the night the forest fire continued to burn. The southbound lanes of the motorway were closed, making space for fire engines that aimed their hoses across the hard shoulder and into the woodland. From above, helicopters dropped water transported from far away lakes. The sky burned red and it was possible to smell the smoke more than fifty miles away.

Radio bulletins and text messages warned residents throughout the region to keep their windows and doors closed, but even so it was possible to taste the fire. The situation was being monitored, a spokesperson said. Check online for updates, she continued, or keep the radio on. The real danger was if the wind changed direction.

◆   ◆   ◆

That night he slept in his bedroom. From his window he could see across the gardens of the neighbours to the darkness of the forest. He wanted to be able to see the fire coming. He left the radio on low, graveyard-shift DJs talking softly between the maudlin and melancholy tunes that he didn't hear. He had ears only for the news bulletins every half an hour but there was no change in the story. The wind stayed the same. The fire continued to burn, but they had it under control. No evacuation order had been issued.

He must have drifted off, because when the explosions began, he woke with a start. It was the sound of New Year's Eve transplanted to high summer. The loud, singular bang of a rocket. The crackle of a sparkler. The whine of a Catherine wheel. He looked out across the gardens, but the forest remained black. He saw lights come on in the surrounding houses. People standing at windows. A message on his phone: they were to gather at the village hall. Buses would be waiting. A news bulletin interrupting a song: the villages were to be emptied. The fire was getting close.

He left the house just as a particularly loud explosion shook the ground around him. On the street, people moved quickly, hurrying towards the church and the village hall, where blue lights flashed against the brick walls. He gave his name to a man in a high-vis jacket holding a clipboard, and climbed onto the bus. He said hello to those neighbours he recognised.

Was his dad still out of town?

He could remember the question hanging between them. A paragraph break.

He nodded, and moved down the aisle to find an empty seat.

Plugging his headphones into his phone, he tuned back in to the radio. They were talking about the explosions. The firefighting effort was being hampered by a number of wartime munitions that had lain, undetected and undisturbed, for decades, but which were now detonating in the heat. The motorway had been completely closed, to be used by vehicles from the fire brigade, police and the military. Empty lanes had become the domain of boar, deer and other animals of the forest, forced out onto the tarmac by the heat and the explosions. A wolf was spotted, the reporter said, stalking the central reservation.

The fire was revealing the secrets of the forest.

♦ ♦ ♦

They were taken north, to the campus of a high school in the nearest market town, where camp beds and blankets had been laid out in the sports hall. It was about four in the morning, but nobody was sleeping. He found an empty bed in the corner and pulled his book out of his bag. Engaged in the story, he didn't notice the man approaching. If he didn't mind, the man said, there were a few questions he needed to ask.

Full name. Date of birth. Place of birth. Address. Father's name. Mother's name.

And where were his parents?

His mother was dead. She died three years before.

The man nodded.

And his father?

He shrugged. Looked back down at his book. Later, he could remember the feeling. He wished he could go into the book. Be surrounded by its pages. Protected.

The man asked the question again. When he would tell me the story later, the boy couldn't remember what he said next. But he had known at the time that this was the moment. It had been coming. It had been coming for months, since the day his father told him he was going for a walk in the woods. That he shouldn't follow. A kiss on the top of his head, a fraction longer than normal, as if his father wanted to imprint something on his son with his lips. As if he wanted him to remember.

His father left the house then, walking off into the forest where the tree trunks now burned and old grenades exploded, and the boars and the wolves fled to the motorway as the flames threatened the houses of the village.

What was the answer? he asked himself later. What did you say to the man in the sports hall? He couldn't remember. The question would be repeated in the days and weeks that followed. An answer of sorts would be given. But it didn't matter. There were some secrets that the forest refused to give up. It was still protecting them.

# DEVIL'S LAKE

I still swim in Devil's Lake, even in high summer when the water is thick and soupy, and I can't see my hand more than a few centimetres below the surface. Many people don't like to swim in the lake like this, when it feels like you need a power hose to get it off you even once you are sitting back on the embankment, but when we were children we were warned off swimming in the Devil's Lake at any time, even when the water was clear and you could see all the way down to the sandy lake floor.

It was not my parents who warned me. They came from elsewhere, and knew nothing of the deep-rooted tales that clung to the clay banks of the lake, like those that occupied the cracks of the ruined house by the railway tracks and the echoing halls of an abandoned factory on the edge of town. There were many stories about the lake: the girl who lived in its depths, tempting solitary travellers standing at the edge into the warm waters, from which they would never return; the creature with razor-sharp teeth that would drag you down by the legs, never to be seen again; dead soldiers, dumped in the water during the final bloody battle of the last great war, succumbing to a watery grave far from home.

Only the last one made me even slightly nervous when I was younger, swimming out to the centre of Devil's Lake, surrounded by the forest. My friends told me that any dead soldiers who had ended up in there would be long gone by the time we went swimming. Fish food. And in any case, one of my friends said, we would have walked over hundreds of dead bodies in the forest on the way there. She had been studying the history of the area for a school project, and she was correct. Throughout the forest between the lake and the town there were numerous small crosses at the foot of the trees, marking the final resting places of soldiers. It had been a battlefield in many wars, not only the last one, and the forest had swallowed many bodies.

It was all sacred ground. Death leaves a mark, whether those who survive choose to make their own or not. Some people feel it more than others. But it's there, as if impregnated in the bark of the trees or soaked into the soil.

◆　◆　◆

I soon stopped thinking about the soldiers, or the beast, or the girl and her siren song. I would swim out and float on the surface, looking up at the sky and the birds that crossed it as my friends chatted in the shallows. Eventually they would call me in, and we would walk back through the woods to town, our hair staining wet our T-shirts as our feet squelched in their sandals.

Now, I have to drive to take a swim in Devil's Lake and I am always alone. I still have contact with all of those friends, but none of them live close enough to join me. And when I meet new people now, it doesn't feel like a question I can ask.

*Should we go for a walk in the forest, and then swim naked in the Devil's Lake?*

It is always possible to scare people off, even if they don't know what might be lurking beneath the surface.

# LONG MEMORY

When the beech was planted, some 150 years ago, the estate had been in the family for nearly two centuries. It had been established in the midst of a wave of settlement that followed a devastating war, when almost half the population had been killed or moved away, and entire villages were abandoned to the forest, never to be recovered. Over the years the family helped create a new village, one that surrounded the main house as a place for the estate workers to live and worship, with fields to the north and the woods to the south providing a barrier to the rest of the world.

Over the decades the family tried many different ways to maintain what fortune they had, from a sheep farming experiment that fell afoul of disease, to an idea for growing exotic fruits that left the estate with an elaborate network of glasshouses designed to trick the trees and other plants into thinking they were growing many degrees further south than they actually were. The greenhouses were built but the plan was never put into action. The head of the family died of complications relating to syphilis contracted in his teenage years, and his son, perhaps less addled than his father, put a stop to the scheme. He saw the future of the family less in ever-more-ambitious agricultural projects and more in the judicious marrying of his offspring, a plan which worked, for a generation or two at least.

When the beech was about fifty years old, the monarchy collapsed, sending shockwaves through the landowning families who saw the old order threatened. They managed to hang on for a couple of decades, but by the time their fears were eventually realised the family had already been scattered, to battlefields where they were buried where they fell and to distant lands where the venerated name no longer opened the doors it once did. Of those who stayed, there was loss and loneliness, and in the case of one family member, a bullet to his own head, his uniform and flag laid out on the floor next to him.

Where once the gardeners and huntsmen had rested in the shadow of the beech tree, it was now shut away in a restricted zone, accessed only by the guards who patrolled the perimeter of a secretive training college. It was in the college's interest for the forest to grow thick and dense, a natural barrier to help hide it away. A new road was laid, with guardhouses at either end; the workers' cottages were supplemented with new buildings on the foundations of the now-removed glasshouses. Some of the workers were kept on, but most had been scattered like the family who had once employed them, and soon there were few who could remember, let alone tell stories of how it had been on the estate before.

Time passed. Another system fell. The guards left and there was no one left to train, and the manor house fell into disrepair. The forest was tidied up, though, and new generations came to discover the beech tree, standing in its own little hollow, a few hundred metres from the first houses of the village. There, things had moved on once more. A clinic. New housing. A primary school for the children of the incomers, and the youngest would take daily walks through the forest, tracking the seasons and taking a rest in the hollow beneath the beech tree.

Can you imagine the stories this tree could tell, the teacher asked one day, as the children played in the dry leaves at its base. And they could. Tales of elves and princes, of animals that talk and humans that don't. Of wolves that howl at the full moon, ghostly apparitions that turn out to be friendly, and cheerful strangers that most certainly don't. One boy imagined building a house in the highest of branches. He would live up there, he said, and grow everything he needed to eat in boxes like the ones his mum kept out the back of their house. He would never need to return to the ground.

If we were to cut down the tree, the teacher continued – to loud boos from the children – we could learn some things about what it had lived through. We could see how old it is. We could tell how the weather had been in different years and across the decades. It was possible, the teacher said, to see how the world was getting warmer, just through the rings of the tree.

But we would have to kill it to know for sure, one of the girls said, and as a group the children circled the tree, to see how many of them it would take to embrace it completely, to protect it from whatever threat might be lurking in the shadows.

# RUINENLUST

My mother, who enjoyed Rome far more than I ever did, used to say that ruins predict the future. They give us a sense of how the world, or a particular version of the world, will look after we've gone. Some ruins, made famous by artists and painters, have been collectively celebrated for their melancholy beauty as fallen artefacts from a lost civilisation, far longer than they were ever used for the purpose for which they were built.

There are architects who, in their idle moments, wonder how their greatest creations will turn out once the roof comes off and the walls begin to fall down. It must surely influence them in the moment they approach the drawing board.

This makes me uneasy, celebrating ruins for their looks alone. How can we celebrate abandoned places simply for their aesthetics, adding filters to our photographs before we post on our social media accounts, without properly understanding why a place became a ruin in the first place? War. Reformation. Family breakdown. Fire. Death. Bankruptcy. Economic crisis. Unemployment. Migration. Kingdoms crushed. Empires fallen. The story matters.

And yet, in the forest, I search them out. The old factory building where plants push up through gaps in the concrete and vines curl around rusting gate posts. An old sanitorium, where cracked tiles and elaborate pipe networks exposed to the elements remind us how futuristic the place once was. And deep in the forest, recognisable only to those who know what they are looking for, a pile of white stones that represent all that is left of a church that once stood at the heart of a village, whose name can still be found on maps.

Sometimes I see the day trippers, out from the city with their cameras and other equipment, climbing through holes in the fence at the old brewery or pushing through the brambles of the brick house by the railway. From the path, the house looks small. A signalman's cottage, perhaps. But if you make your way through the tangle, you'll soon see that what you thought was a cottage is simply an outhouse, that the main building stands behind, not quite hidden by the bushes and trees.

When we were young, the house was already abandoned, and those heading through the tunnel on their way to parties in the forest would quicken their step as they passed by, even if they never mentioned it to each other or spoke about why. I went that way myself. In the day. At dusk. With the first light of morning. But ruins didn't scare me then and they don't scare me now. I'd just like to know the story.

I search out some of the photographs online. Some are hyper realistic, and it's possible to make out the texture of the peeling wallpaper and each individual splinter in a fallen beam. Others are in black and white. Others apply a filter, to make the photograph look old-fashioned, as if from another time or place. And yes, some of them try to provide a context for their images, for their *Ruinenlust*, by telling a story of this house by the railway tracks, even though there is no agreement as to what the story might be.

I don't know either, and it annoys me.

It comes grudgingly, but I have to admit there is an attraction to these photographs that I find online, not dissimilar to how I feel when I explore the place in person. I too find the images beautiful in their decay, in how they remind us and how they offer up a warning. Still, I want to know. Who lived there? Why did they leave? Who owns the house now? Why has it been left to ruin?

The last time I was there, I found evidence of a gathering in one of the back rooms. Empty bottles and a small fire pit. It was winter, and there was a light dusting of snow on the ground. On the wall someone had painted a series of messages. Most were indecipherable to me. Perhaps I am too old. But there was one which was clear.

EXTINCTION IS COMING.

I sat down on the windowsill and looked out from the ruined house and into the forest. All the bottles at my feet were empty, and I hadn't thought to bring one of my own.

# CATAPULT

I met the couple the day they moved into the house next to mine. It wasn't long after she'd been released from hospital, and she still walked carefully, as if unsure whether her legs were truly able to take her weight. Her partner I'd seen before, directing painters and decorators, meeting with electricians and delivery men, as he rushed to get the house ready for moving-in day. He came out from the city by train, he told me once, over the fence, coming after work or using days of annual leave to meet his appointments. He could have asked me, I told him, but he just nodded and then never did.

The day after they moved in, she came round to my side of the house to say hello. She was, she said, really pleased to be moving into the village, and she hoped that once things settled down, we would have some time to get to know each other. It was nice, I thought at the time, that she was so open. It wasn't always the way in the village. I remember hoping that she would be able to keep this openness in the face of the experiences that were sure to come, that the surly, unspoken suspicion of the outsider would not cause her to retreat into herself.

They'd moved out to our village, she continued, because they felt it was the perfect place for her to recover. The way she said it suggested to me that it had been his idea, and she was yet to be convinced. Walks in the woods would help build her strength. The air was better. It was quiet, and that was better for her writing. And she could do that anywhere. It was her partner she felt sorry for, she said, looking straight at me. He would travel back and forth each day to the city. She would stay, to concentrate on her work and her recovery in peace.

◆　◆　◆

That first summer, as we grew accustomed to living in proximity to each other, sharing a wall and the garden fence, things seemed to be going well. He worked and she wrote, and they would meet in the garden when he came in from the train, and they would sit in the shadow of an apple tree that reached from my side of the fence across into their garden. I told them that when the time came, they should help themselves to the fruit. I couldn't possibly eat them all. A couple of times they invited me over for a barbecue and a drink. He liked beer, gathering the green bottles in the grass at his feet as he went. She preferred wine, red or white, poured into a plastic beaker. I had already noted this from my side of the fence, so I knew what to bring with me when the invitation came.

Some evenings I saw them walk out from the house at dusk, heading towards the gravel track that led from the main road to the forest. I watched as she grew steadier on her feet, her posture more assured, her stride longer and more confident. With each step I could see her moving further from that hospital bed, leaving the ward and the memory of those months behind her.

Over the winter she took to walking once a day to the shops, taking a break from work in the early afternoon. On her way home she would ring my doorbell and I would prepare coffee to have with the cake or pastries she brought. We would spend an hour together at my kitchen table before she walked around the house to her own front door and climbed the stairs to her study. I could hear her from my side of the wall. Some days her walk was longer, starting not long after he left for the train. On those days she would arrive at my door red-faced and glowing, her boots splattered with mud or damp from the snow. They didn't walk together in the evenings anymore. It was too dark, by the time he got home from the city. She didn't seem to mind. She seemed to me just as happy to walk on her own.

Did it bother him? I asked her once, but she shook her head and said she didn't think so. In any case, as she told him, he was always with her. I suppose he took it to mean that she always held him close, but the way she told me meant I couldn't be entirely sure.

◆  ◆  ◆

One morning he didn't take the train to work. They left for a walk together, and when they returned there was no cake in her hand or knock at the door. Later, I watched from my window as she walked down the drive to a waiting taxi. She put her bag in the boot and got into the back seat. She didn't look back. He stayed in the house for a few more days, but then he too was gone. I presume he decided there was no point making such a long commute if she was no longer out there, waiting for him to come home. The house stood empty for a few months until my current neighbours moved in, another couple, also quite friendly, although I haven't yet offered them a free run at my apple tree.

About a year after they left, she knocked at my door. She had brought me cake, and a copy of her latest book. She was so sorry, she said, as she slipped her boots off in the porch, that she hadn't come sooner to say goodbye. At the kitchen table I poured out her coffee as if she'd never been away and then asked her what had happened.

He still saw her as the girl lying in the hospital bed, she said. He still thought she needed saving. Needed looking after. She didn't need to tell me any more, so I asked her instead about her book and her new life on the coast, and listened as she told me of her afternoon walks and how the forest on the island reminded her of here.

That evening I sat down in my armchair and read her book in one sitting. It was a book of stories, fragments really, of people and places. It was fiction, but it was possible to see the places where her imagination met reality and they combined. I could see myself in one character, and I was flattered. And as I continued to read, I felt that I was now joining her on those walks, following the gravel track, heading through the forest. I could see the journey that she made, travelling a little further each time. In the beginning she did take him with her, but by the end, as the story moved gently towards its conclusion, he was completely absent. When she shook the snow from her boots for the final time it was over. There was no space left. She had let him go.

# LOST & FOUND

*Contents of an old shopping bag emptied into the bin, having been collected on a walk through the forest on the second weekend of April. All contents noted down for a letter to be written to the local newspaper:*

Single hiking boot, laces frayed.

Half empty can of dog food.

Deodorant canister.

Empty bottle of vodka.

Bobble hat. Red.

Tin foil. Three pieces.

Crisp packet.

Pair of ankle socks, light blue.

Half-eaten chocolate bar (supermarket own brand).

Empty condom wrapper.

Bent metal prongs (the kind you find at a garden centre in the barbecue section).

Beer bottle. Czech lager. Empty.

Child's glove, white.

Teaspoon.

Handful of damp circus flyers, dated last December.

Deflated helium balloon. Minnie Mouse.

Shotgun cartridge.

A scented candle, found at the base of a giant beech tree, flickering in the half-light of a spring afternoon.

# THREE

# THE HUNTER'S PULPIT

I climb up the uneven ladder and into the hunter's pulpit, half-hidden on the edge of the forest, surrounded by silver birches and with a view out across the fields. It is not mine, this high hunting chair, made out of wood and so resembling a birdwatcher's hide. And why wouldn't it? They have the same intention, after all. To spot our fellow living creatures without being spotted ourselves.

I like to climb up into the hunter's pulpit because, in all truth, in recent times I have discovered that, although I am not exactly old, I can no longer climb trees in the way I did in my youth, and this seems to me to be the next best thing. Up here the smell reminds me of those days. The musty, semi-sweet tang of things rotting beneath me. The sound is similar, of trees moving and creaking, leaves shaking. And it feels the same too, as the pulpit sways in the wind, like a boat in gentle waters.

I sit up here with my back to the forest, listening to the sound of the trees as I gaze out across the fields. I have no gun at my side, and I am no danger to the deer that I spot, nor the cranes or the hooded crows. I can sit up here for hours, protected from any rain that might fall by the pulpit roof, fortified with coffee and a bag of sandwiches. I sometimes wonder if, during hunting season, the man – and I assume it is a man – who is responsible for this structure notices any clues of my presence? The stones that he uses to balance his own flask moved to a different corner of the platform. Crumbs, wedged between the planks of wood at his feet. The spot where I absentmindedly scraped off a small patch of moss, the hunter's pulpit version of doodling on the notepad kept by the phone. I'm like a ghost; haunting him, whether he knows it or not.

◆  ◆  ◆

When I was a child I was fascinated by these structures. Everyone loves the idea of a treehouse. Later, during a period where I found it distasteful to eat meat, and somehow suspected most hunters of being the potential paramilitary wing of a terrible new regime, I thought them ugly and threatening, blights on what I considered to be an otherwise natural landscape.

*Landscape.* The word disqualifies the adjective that comes before it. The hunter's pulpit is no more alien a presence than the water tower or the brick church, the ploughed field or the pine plantation. The land has been shaped and 'scaped for so long there is nothing I can see from here, where I sit high in the hunter's pulpit surrounded by young trees, that has not felt the influence of human hands. And I've grown more tolerant of hunters, too. I still wonder about them, in their military garb, but my freezer is filled with what they bring home, and if they are committing a crime it is nothing compared to what takes place in the giant torture and killing sheds for chickens and pigs. The men who run them might not look like paramilitaries, but they have far more blood on their hands.

So, I hope he would not mind, this hunter, if he ever discovered I use his pulpit at times when he doesn't need it. And he must know what it is that brings me up here. He must understand, feel it himself. For if he was driven only by bloodlust, by the thrill of the kill, then there would be other and easier ways to feed it. No, he sits up here for hour upon hour, waiting for his target to appear, much as I do, leaning against the same rough, wooden wall, waiting for mine. A red kite. A rough-legged buzzard. Those elegant cranes.

Could you ever pull the trigger?

I imagine him speaking to me as I pick out two young deer with my binoculars. I shake my head, even though he isn't here to see it. And in this moment, I can tell that the hunter and my previous self would be in agreement, and I can only confirm that yes, indeed, I am a hypocrite.

◆ ◆ ◆

My favourite time in the pulpit is high summer, on one of those thick, heavy days when it feels like you can hold the air in your hands and roll it into a ball, as the sky seems to close in, glowing on the horizon, only this time it is not a forest fire but the anticipation of the coming storm. And then it darkens, as if the world itself is about to end, and the rain and wind and lightning comes and the thunder rolls across the land we have created, and high in the hunter's pulpit I wrap a blanket round my shoulders, lean forward, and through the gap in the wood created for a rifle, I watch the show.

# WATERING CANS

When her husband died, he was buried, as he wished, in the cemetery on the edge of town. It was nominally Protestant, this forest cemetery, but there proved to be no real obstacles in obtaining a place for him. She remembered the funeral so very clearly, even though it was now nearly twenty years since he left her.

It was a spring day. Often, when people think of spring, they think of it as a colourful season. And it can be, in the gardens and meadows, once it has had a chance to take hold. But sometimes, when you feel the warmth of the first proper spring day, you can also sense, lurking in the background, the winter clinging on. It hides in the shadows of the trees, not yet ready to relinquish its hold completely. It was one of those days, and she shivered through most of it.

Twenty years. Nearly two decades of walking through the town from where they had lived together in a flat above the bakery that had once been theirs. When retirement came, they sold the business but kept the flat. People told them it was now their chance, they could move out to the edge of town or one of the villages, a house with a garden, where they could enjoy their peace. But it all sounded like too much work, and anyway, they liked that they could walk to the shops, to the pub and the train station, the doctor's surgery and the post office. And once he was gone, there was the walk to the cemetery to consider, too. So, no. It was better to stay put, and so she did, and that was that.

◆ ◆ ◆

In all the years of coming to the cemetery, there are still a few things that she doesn't understand. The modern fashion for photographs on headstones, for example. It seems a strange choice to her. Unless it is a baby, the thought of which just makes her shudder, how do you even begin to choose a photograph that should represent a whole life? It's impossible.     Another     thing     is     the watering cans at the entrance. Everyone has their own, locked to a stand with a cheap bicycle lock. Twenty years she has been coming here, and still she does not get why everyone needs to have their own. Why not just five or six, waiting for whoever needs to use them? Either people were stealing them, which is depressing in one way, or people don't like the idea of others using their precious watering cans, which is depressing in another. And she has witnessed arguments in the past, fights over flowers and flower beds, or the noise of a cheerful child being scolded by a stranger. People say cemeteries are sad places, and she agrees, but she thinks it is the living that make them so, not the dead.

It is funny, when she thinks about it now, that he was so insistent on being buried here. Unlike her, he was actually from the town, a true country man who could identify plants and trees, animal tracks in the snow and what the weather was going to do, and all with the confidence that only comes with being properly ignorant. God love him. Who knows if he was right? Certainly not her, but it made him happy when she accepted his wisdom, even though there were many times when she was fairly sure he was muddling up his species and the promised rainstorm never came. In any case, wasn't that what you were supposed to do? Wasn't that what she had been taught?

Nowadays she cannot walk the whole way to the cemetery, so she takes the bus. And because she takes the bus, she has more energy when she gets there to walk a little, from the gate in the back fence of the cemetery and into the forest. She still cannot tell her beech from her birch, her oak from her sycamore or her fir from her pine, and they are the moments she misses him most, misses him bending down to pick up a leaf, as if it holds within it all the answers to whichever question might come next. Then he would say, with confidence and a gentle pat on the trunk, that this is indeed a beech tree, and a fine specimen too. If only it could tell us everything it has seen, he would say, and then amble on along the path.

She has nearly twenty years of stories to tell.

At the cemetery, she unlocks the watering can, *her* watering can, from the fence by the small chapel and makes her way to his grave. It was a simple headstone she chose. She likes to sit on the bench, a few metres away, and look at it. She doesn't talk to him here. For all his insistence that this was the place where he wanted to be, she knows he isn't here. Twenty years of stories. He'll have to wait a little while longer yet.

# ASHES (IN THE PINES)

I always knew that the gravel pathways, green watering cans and colourful flowers were not for me. I wanted to be deeper in the forest. Scattered and swallowed; returned. A mix of trees. Plenty of life. Plenty of company. A good place to rest.

# Acknowledgements

## Paul

I would like to thank Gary, Sanya, Kit and all at Influx Press for helping bring this project out into the world. Thanks to my family and friends, especially those who have explored the forest with me. Thanks to Nadine Khouri for her beautiful songs, including one which inspired one of the stories in this book. Thanks to Eymelt for her photographs, works of art that helped shape the words on the page. Finally, thanks to Katrin and Lotte, my favourite companions for heading into the woods.

## Eymelt

I would like to thank Paul for coming up with this fantastic and inspiring idea to collaborate, letting me contribute my photographs to his words and stories. Paul can also bear witness to how boring it is to be my photo assistant. Without Ólafur Örn Arnarson's patience and driving skills, my mobile photo lab would have never made it safe into the woods and back. He endured hardship in all sorts of weather. I am also indebted to my gallery manager Mariagrazia Riccio for lending me a strong shoulder and giving me digital advice in my all-analogue world. Getting my analogue plates into a printable digital format is a craft that Termindruck in Berlin understand best. Thanks to Mario Kohler and his colleagues there. Very many thanks to the rock'n'roll publishers at Influx Press in London, especially Gary Budden with his fairy tale and folklore interest and inspiration. Finally, I'd love to thank my parents Eymelt and Thomas Sehmer for supporting me in my endeavours and my granny Eymelt Müller who always encouraged me to go my own way.

# About the Author

PAUL SCRATON is a Lancashire-born writer and editor based in Berlin. Paul is the editor-in-chief of *Elsewhere: A Journal of Place* and the author of *Ghosts on the Shore: Travels Along Germany's Baltic Coast* (Influx Press, 2017) and the novel *Built on Sand* (Influx Press, 2019).

His essays on place and memory have been published as the pocket book *The Idea of a River: Walking out of Berlin* (Readux Books, 2015), and in *Mauerweg: Stories from the Berlin Wall Trail* (Slow Travel Berlin, 2014).

Elsewhere, his work has appeared in *The Lonely Crowd*, *New Statesman*, Literary Hub, Caught by the River, *SAND Journal* and *hidden europe magazine*, among others.

T: @underagreysky W: underagreysky.com

# About the Photographer

EYMELT SEHMER is a Berlin based professional photographer, artist and filmmaker. Growing up in a densely wooded area in West Germany the forest always fuelled her imagination.

In her works she mainly focuses on mythology, fairy tales and folklore. She is particularly interested in old analogue photographic techniques. Together with Icelandic artist Mr. Arnarson she runs an art gallery and photo studio in Berlin.

*In the Pines* is her second collaboration with writer Paul Scraton. For this book she made Paul drag her mobile darkroom through the woods of Brandenburg. Yet, she hopes that there will be more projects with Paul to come.

## About the photography

For the photographs, Eymelt used the collodion wet plate process. This is one of the very early photography techniques that requires, for example, that a black tin plate be coated, sensitised, exposed and developed within the span of about ten to fifteen minutes. Eymelt worked with a portable darkroom in the field as photographic images needed to be developed while the plate was still wet. Eymelt prepared the collodion emulsion and all the chemistry herself, and each plate was coated and developed by hand, resulting in slight imperfections as well as an eerie look. This was an entirely analogue process and every photographic plate was handmade – no photoshop was involved. Although the original technique uses quite toxic chemicals, Eymelt focused on finding alternatives that are more environmentally friendly. For the book, the plates were scanned in high resolution with a high-end photo scanner.

# About the photography

INFLUX
PRESS

Influx Press is an independent publisher based in London, committed to publishing innovative and challenging literature from across the UK and beyond.

Lifetime supporters: Bob West and Barbara Richards

www.influxpress.com
@Influxpress